Deep Sea
Dentist

'Deep Sea Dentist'
An original concept by Jenny Moore
© Jenny Moore 2021

Illustrated by Izzy Evans

Published by MAVERICK ARTS PUBLISHING LTD
Studio 11, City Business Centre, 6 Brighton Road,
Horsham, West Sussex, RH13 5BB
© Maverick Arts Publishing Limited November 2021
+44 (0)1403 256941

A CIP catalogue record for this book is available at the British Library.

ISBN 978-1-84886-834-2

Maverick
publishing
www.maverickbooks.co.uk

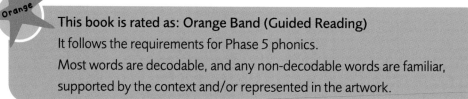

This book is rated as: Orange Band (Guided Reading)
It follows the requirements for Phase 5 phonics.
Most words are decodable, and any non-decodable words are familiar,
supported by the context and/or represented in the artwork.

Deep Sea Dentist

by Jenny Moore

illustrated by
Izzy Evans

Instead of a white coat,

Dawn the dentist has...

...a diving costume!

Instead of a black chair that lifts

up and down, Dawn has...

...a boat!

Dawn is a deep sea dentist!

There are lots of teeth to look after

in the sea.

Here comes a fish now. It's a Fangtooth.

His teeth are very long and spiky.

"Hello, have you come for your check-up?" Dawn smiles. "No biting," she adds. "Those fangs look super sharp!"

"Good!" Dawn grins. "I can see you've been looking after your teeth."

She hands him a sticker.

"Keep up the good work. And don't forget your gums!"

Next to arrive is a fish with LOTS of teeth.

It's a shark!

13

"I can see lots of new teeth today,"

she tells her.

"Sharks grow new teeth all the time

to replace the ones that fall out."

Dawn thinks the shark tooth fairy must have a hard job.

A shark can have up to thirty thousand teeth in its life!

"Don't forget to brush each row of teeth twice every day," Dawn smiles. The shark chooses a sticker and flashes Dawn a tooth-filled grin.

"Who's next?" asks Dawn.

A big, dark shadow looms

over her.

It's a whale! He looks upset.

"What's wrong?" asks Dawn.

"Have you got a painful tooth?"

The whale nods his huge head.

"Oh dear," murmurs Dawn. "Let's take a look, shall we?"

The whale stretches his giant jaws.

Dawn shines her dentist torch round

his mouth.

"There!" she cries. "I see what the

matter is!"

"You've got something stuck between

your teeth," Dawn explains.

She reaches in and pulls out a long stick...

It's a fishing rod!

"Is that better?" Dawn asks the whale.

He nods his head.

"Try and remember to floss every day,"
Dawn tells him.

"Flossing helps get rid of stuck food...
and fishing rods!"

Dawn hands the whale an extra big sticker for being so brave.

She gives herself a sticker too.

You have to be very brave to be a

deep sea dentist!

Quiz

1. Instead of a white coat, Dawn has...
a) ...a diving costume
b) ...a black chair
c) ...some goggles

2. What kind of teeth does the Fangtooth have?
a) Small and pointy
b) Short and round
c) Long and spiky

3. What does Dawn give each sea creature?
a) A lollipop
b) A toothbrush
c) A sticker

4. What is stuck in the whale's teeth?
a) A fishing rod
b) A broom
c) A branch

5. What helps get rid of stuck food?
a) Eating
b) Stickers
c) Flossing

Turn over for answers

Book Bands for Guided Reading

The Institute of Education book banding system is a scale of colours that reflects the various levels of reading difficulty. The bands are assigned by taking into account the content, the language style, the layout and phonics. Word, phrase and sentence level work is also taken into consideration.

Maverick Early Readers are a bright, attractive range of books covering the pink to white bands. All of these books have been book banded for guided reading to the industry standard and edited by a leading educational consultant.

To view the whole Maverick Readers scheme, visit our website at

www.maverickearlyreaders.com

Or scan the QR code above to view our scheme instantly!

Quiz Answers: 1a, 2c, 3c, 4a, 5c